SCARY
STORY STARTERS

By Diane Cuneo

Illustrated by Kerry L. Manwaring

Lowell House
Juvenile
Los Angeles

CONTEMPORARY BOOKS
Chicago

To Erik, Caley, & Rosalind,
Kids So Terrific, It's Scary.
—D.C.

Requests for such permissions should be addressed to:
Lowell House Juvenile
2029 Century Park East, Suite 3290
Los Angeles, CA 90067

Publisher: Jack Artenstein
Vice President/General Manager, Juvenile Division: Elizabeth Amos
Director of Publishing Services: Rena Copperman
Editorial Director: Brenda Pope-Ostrow
Art Director: Lisa Theresa-Lenthall
Typesetter: Carolyn Wendt

Lowell House books can be purchased at special discounts
when ordered in bulk for premiums and special sales.
Contact Department JH at the above address.

Manufactured in the United States of America

ISBN: 1-56565-313-0

10 9 8 7 6 5 4 3 2 1

note to parents

For those children who love a good scare—and who love to scare others—**SCARY STORY STARTERS** is a workbook that will promote both creativity and enjoyment. It contains a strong mix of creative writing and story-telling exercises on several levels. While each exercise is enhanced by black-line drawings, in some cases your child is encouraged to do his or her own spooky illustrations.

Remember that children who do not yet have the language and spelling skills necessary to write full, "correct" sentences are nonetheless more than capable of expressing their ideas phonetically and need to be challenged to do so.

Throughout **SCARY STORY STARTERS,** story "skeletons" are provided for your child to "flesh" out. Please work with your child and encourage him or her to do the exercises in order. This will help the child go on to write full, complete stories. Your child should first finish the fill-in-the-blank sentences by choosing words from provided lists, or by choosing words of his or her own. Then, for several writing exercises, your child is asked to write the beginning, middle, or end of a terrifying tale, thereby learning valuable information on the art of sequential story-telling. The child will discover the distinctions between these three parts of a story and the unique role each plays in telling a *good* ghostly story.

Designed to promote fun, creativity, and self-confidence, and to develop such skills as language arts, story-telling, sequential relationships, logic, reasoning, and lots more, **SCARY STORY STARTERS** is sure to be a success with you and your child.

How Scary Are You?

Read the short stories below. They each need an ending. Write the number of the ending you would choose on the line following each story. The scarier your ending, the higher your score! When you are done, add up your points to find out how scary YOU can be!

Brad, the school bully, took the shy new student's hat. When Brad got home, he put it on. Suddenly, _____

1. he looked taller.
2. the hat became stuck and wouldn't come off.
3. the hat swallowed him whole, then spit out his bones.

Jacob woke up and heard a strange noise coming from his closet. He looked in the closet and _____

1. saw his puppy, Buster.
2. saw a ghost, but it turned out to be an old coat.
3. was grabbed by a hairy claw and never seen again.

Caley didn't believe in vampires until _____

1. she was ten.
2. she saw one in a movie.
3. her mom turned into a vampire with bloody fangs.

The mail carrier always wore his hat low over his face. The neighborhood kids dared Kyle to pull it off. When he did, Kyle saw that the mail carrier _____

1. had blue eyes.
2. had glowing red eyes.
3. had three eyes.

The kids in Mrs. Franklin's class thought their teacher just had a little cold until she _____

1. sneezed and got everyone wet.
2. coughed up worms.
3. turned into a giant lizard and ate the whole class.

Misha and Jamal were not supposed to open Grandpa's old box. But when they took off the lid, _____

1. they discovered old candy wrappers.
2. they found a dried-up apple that looked like a shrunken head.
3. they found a finger that was still twitching.

The new baby-sitter looked strange, but the kids' mom and dad had to hurry to the school-board meeting. When they got back, _____

1. the kids were eating burned popcorn.
2. the kids were eating frogs.
3. the kids WERE frogs.

When the soccer ball rolled into the street sewer, only Jakeem was brave enough to climb in. Unfortunately, _____

1. his shoes got muddy.
2. his leg was bitten off.
3. it took three weeks to find all the body parts.

As a slumber party prank, the girls tried to braid Jacqui's hair while she was sleeping. But on the back of her head, they were horrified to find _____

1. a tattoo of George Washington.
2. a hole with a water bug in it.
3. a grinning mouth with maggots coming out of it.

Now add up your score by using the numbers next to the endings you chose. For each time you chose ending number 1, you get 1 point. You get 2 points for each time you chose ending number 2, and you get 3 points for each time you chose ending number 3. The higher your score, the scarier YOU are!

How Scary Are You?

1-10   You call that scary?

11-18   You could scare a baby . . . maybe.

19-26   You sure know how to scare a person!

27   Horrors! You are the scariest!!

Here, draw a picture of your scariest ending.

DRAWN BY _____

make your own monster!

Find the word list that matches the number under each blank. Use any word from that list to fill in the blank—or use your OWN word. When you are finished, you will have a scary monster you can call your own!

In my scary story, my monster would have _____ eyes,
                                                    1

_____ legs, _____ arms, and _____ heads! My
    1   1   1

monster's body would be covered with _____. My monster
                                            2

would have _____ instead of teeth! My monster's breath
              2

would smell like _____. My monster would be afraid of
                    3

only one thing: _____. My monster gets really mad when
                    4

people throw _____ at it. Don't throw _____ at MY
                5   5

monster, or it will _____ you! My monster's name would
                        6

be _____.
    7

Here, draw a picture of something YOUR monster would eat.

DRAWN BY _____

WORD LISTS

1. fat, bug-filled, two, inside-out, skinny, seven, no, a million, melting, black, three, bloody, exploding, purple, ten, bulging

2. rubber bands, slobber, spikes, teeth, worms, maggots, blood, razors, slime, trees, baseball bats, lizards, rocks, raisins, cards, windows

3. dirty diapers, garlic, death, spoiled milk, rotten eggs, cow pies, my brother, my sister, my socks, a garbage dump

4. mice, redheads, its shadow, hot dogs, holes, a spanking, rain, magic, cole slaw, TV, me, ghosts, vampires, crosses, yarmulkes, the ace of spades

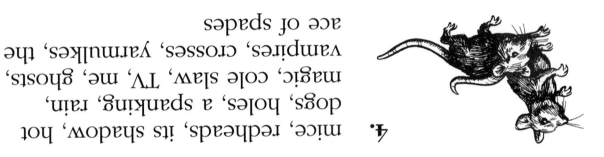

5. sticks, rocks, fire, water, people, trash, mountains, toasters, fairy dust, homework, blood, toes, hair spray, clock radios, backpacks

6. eat, scare, step on, rip, sit on, harm, melt, bury, sing to, kick, bite, trip, scold, squash, kidnap, burn, freeze, swallow

7. FrankNBeans, Terrorizer, Louise, Walking Death, Larry, Nukaman, Bob the Burper, ShankNaNa, Total Fat, Crusher, Dead Ringer

create your own scary place

Some places are famous for being scary: a cemetery, a wax museum, a closet, or a basement. But you can use your imagination to make any place a scary place. Match each blank to a word list to create your own fun—and scary!—place.

The place I would pick for the setting of my scary story would be a _____. It would seem safe at first, but then

1

you would see the _____ on the _____. The weather

2

3

outside would be _____. A strange _____ would be

4

5

coming from the _____. The kids in my story would be

3

_____. They would want to get away from this place, but

6

their _____ would be _____ to the ground. In the end,

7

8

the whole place would _____.

9

Here, draw a picture of your scary place.

DRAWN BY _____

WORD LISTS

1. doctor's office, toy store, playground, sock drawer, doll house, birthday party, library, pizza parlor, tree house, school, supermarket, mall

2. blood, hair, lips, guts, syrup, eyeballs, fingers, skeletons, slime, bats, tombstones, teeth, fire, boiling water, coffin

3. ceiling, floor, chairs, instruments, cake, leaves, floor, wall, shelves, desks, doorknob, tube socks, window, roof, swings, oven, books, closet, basement, door

4. freezing, rainy, muggy, calm, murky, overcast, soupy, sunless, subzero, sunny, stinky

5. smell, sound, noise, *boing,* crackle, moan, song, creaking, whistle, animal, monster, man, woman, child, growling

6. scared, sad, stupid, brave, lazy, hungry, curious, confused, helpless, mad, lost, dizzy, frozen

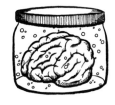

7. feet, hearts, eyes, tongues, clothes, cars, brains, hair, stomachs, backpacks, gifts, socks, shoes, bottoms, lips, bones

8. nailed, burned, frozen, stuck, popping, rolling, twisting, falling, melting, flopping, rotting, bouncing, dancing

9. be swallowed by the earth, disappear, grow up to the sky, blow up, be destroyed

make your own creepy comparisons

When you want to describe something scary, it helps to compare it to something else. This is called a **simile**. A simile helps to get the picture across with words. Do the following exercises and see for yourself! Choose a word when given a choice. Fill in the blank with your own word or words when asked.

Its face was the color of _____

1. mold.

2. pus.

3. midnight.

The werewolf's teeth gleamed like _____

1. diamonds.

2. knives.

3. a stabbing light.

The head rolled across the floor like a _____

1. goldfish bowl.

2. bowling ball.

3. kicked pot.

Now try some similes of your own!

The blood dripped from the box like _____.

The magic dust made her eyes feel like _____.

The ringing in his ears sounded like _____.

He fell off the cliff like a _____.

The boy's leg snapped like a _____.

The bat cave smelled like a _____.

The pile of bodies looked like _____.

Her head spun around like a _____.

He stared at his smashed foot. It looked like _____.

The wizard's laugh cracked through the night like _____.

the monstrous alphabet

Fill in the blanks. The scary word you choose must begin with the letter of the alphabet. The first one has been done for you.

A the chewed **arm**
the **acid** bath

B the _____ witch's pot
the rotting _____

C the bloody _____
the _____ body

D the fiery-eyed _____
the _____ man

E the floating _____
the _____ laugh

F a _____ in his mouth
the _____ eyeball

G a _____ in the closet
it had _____ teeth

H a _____ under the bed
the _____ leg

I a body in the _____
the _____ goo

J fingers in the _____
a _____ monster

K the _____ in the basement
the _____ in his back

L the escaped _____
the _____ in her hair

M a fat, poisonous _____
the _____ bone

N the murderous _____
the _____ in the skull

O an _____ with rabies
the _____ janitor

P the _____ oozed out
the _____ were scattered

Q the Dracula _____
the _____ death

R the narrow _____
the _____ dagger

S the high-pitched _____
the _____ shoe

T the Werewolf's _____
the _____ girl

U the _____ troll
the scary _____

V the bloodthirsty _____
the _____ of blood

W a _____ at the window
the _____ witch

X the haunted _____
the skeleton in the _____

Y a _____ of fear
long, _____ teeth

Z the _____ ghost
the _____ family

fill in the blanks

Now it's time to put your scary monster in your scary place and use your scary descriptions to write a scary story! (Whew!) Use your ideas to fill in the blanks.

A Scary Story

By _____

In a little town called Fearville, a monster ruled the townspeople from a _____ where it lived. The people were afraid, because the monster's body was covered with _____ and its breath smelled like _____. Instead of teeth, the monster had _____. The monster loved to eat _____, so the townspeople had to bring it a wheelbarrow full every week. There was _____ hanging on the _____ where the monster lived. The weather there was always _____, no matter what it was like in the town. Once a man had tried to kill the monster by throwing _____ at it, but the monster got mad and _____ the man. It seemed like Fearville would be ruled forever by this monster, until one day a little girl named _____ noticed something odd.

"I think the monster is afraid," she said.

"The monster is afraid of nothing," said her mother.

"I think it's afraid of _____," said the girl.

Before her mother could stop her, the girl ran to the monster and showed it _____. The monster shrieked in horror and ran to the mountains and was never seen again. The townspeople were so happy, they changed the name of Fearville to _____, which was the girl's name. They called the mountains _____, because that was the monster's name.

The End

Finish the picture!

On the next few pages, the beginnings and middles of spooky stories have been done for you. You have to write each scary ending.

The Bloody Joke

By _____

One day when I was cleaning out the basement, I found an old piece of paper stuck beneath the stairs. When I dusted it off, I found this:

RECIPE FOR STAGE BLOOD
You will need:
• 1½ cups clear Karo syrup • ½ cup warm water
• 4 tablespoons red food coloring • 12 drops green food coloring
To make, just stir and splatter!

"Wow!" I thought. "I can make something that looks and feels like REAL blood!" From upstairs, my bossy sister called down to me: "Hey, goofball! Aren't you finished yet?" She thought she was so cool! I decided to play a joke on her. I mixed the recipe and _____

_____

_____

_____

_____

The End

The Last Ride

By _____

Beth, Kate, and Lopez sat high up in the roller-coaster car, shivering in the night air. The ride had been stopped for a long time. At first, it was fun. But then they could see the lights of the fair dimming, and the people below—who looked like ants—leaving for home. No one was looking for them!

They shouted and shouted, but no one heard them—or so they thought. For just when the fairgrounds seemed empty, the roller coaster suddenly lit up, and the car began to roll faster and faster toward a shadowy figure waiting farther along the tracks.

_____

_____

_____

_____

_____

_____

_____

The End

A Little off the Top

By _____

When Harvey needed a haircut, his mom took him to a new barbershop called Heads. She was trying to save money.

"How cheap is it?" asked Harvey when they arrived.

"The kids' haircuts are free," said his mom.

"Free?" cried Harvey. "How good can the place be?"

His mom said, "How bad can it be? Just give it a chance."

The shop was crowded. When they went inside, a strange lady offered Harvey's mom some tea. "It's nice in here," his mom said, sipping the tea.

Harvey looked around. There were lots of grown-ups but no kids.

"The kids get their heads cut . . . I mean, their hair cut . . . in the other room," said the strange lady, as if reading Harvey's mind.

Harvey saw a door that led to the back room. He heard sawing noises. Then he saw something that looked like blood seeping through the crack under the door!

"Mom! Look!" cried Harvey. But his mom gave him a

blank smile and continued to sip her tea.

"Go with the nice lady," she said in a robot's voice.
Then the woman grabbed Harvey's arm and began to
drag him away. Harvey

_____

_____

_____

_____

_____

_____

_____

_____

_____

_____

_____

_____

_____

_____

_____

_____

The End

Father Knows Flesh

By _____

Brad's dad was a butcher. He paid the rent and bought food and clothing for his family with the money he made in his small shop. But business had been bad lately, and there was not enough money for the rent. The landlord said that if Brad's dad didn't pay up in three days, they would have to move out. The landlord laughed when Brad asked him to be nice to his dad. "Nice guys finish last," he had snarled. Now, as Brad wiped the meat counter, he was worried about their future. Just then, the landlord walked in.

"Pay up, or be out by Tuesday!" the landlord said. The floor squeaked under his weight. He was as big as a toolshed.

"I wonder how much we could get for him a pound," Brad said to his dad, trying to make him laugh.

Brad's dad was silent for a long time. Then he said, "I think it's time for you and your mom to go visit Grandma for a few days. When you get back, our problem will be solved."

Brad's _____

_____

_____

_____

_____

_____

_____

_____

_____

_____

_____

_____

_____

_____

_____

_____

_____

_____

_____

The End

The Boston Cream Pie Strangler

By _____

One sunny day Theo and Tony were walking home from school when a little old lady called out to them from her yard. She was holding a tree branch in her arms and seemed to be staggering under its weight.

"Please help me, children," she called out in a withered voice.

"We're not supposed to talk to strangers," whispered Theo.

Tony laughed. "What can an old lady do to us? Besides, she needs help!" So Tony went to help, and Theo walked on. Later that night, Tony called Theo to brag.

"You missed it," he said. "The old lady invited me in and gave me some Boston Cream Pie. She let me eat all I wanted! I bet I ate two whole pies!"

The next morning Theo got the news that during the night, Tony had started choking and was rushed to the hospital. He had almost choked to death on whipped cream, which was clogging his throat. And the whipped

cream turned out to be poisonous! Theo knew the old lady
had something to do with it, and he went to her house to

_____

_____

_____

_____

_____

_____

_____

_____

_____

_____

_____

_____

_____

_____

_____

_____

_____

The End

The Math Monster

By _____

Cooper was a smart boy, but he was lazy. He never studied, and now school was getting harder and harder. Third grade was tough! His grandmother had taken away his video games until he raised his spelling grades. And if he didn't do well on his math test, he'd be grounded from riding his bike, as well! But every time he tried to study, a lazy thought would interrupt. The night before the math test, when Cooper's grandmother thought he was studying, he was really playing with his Majik Cards.

"I wish I could know the answers without studying!" he said, holding one of the cards.

"You can," whispered an evil voice. Cooper looked down. The hideous green monster on the playing card was talking to him! Cooper screamed and threw the card down.

"Do you want to get one hundred percent on the test or not?"

"I—I do," stuttered Cooper.

"Tomorrow at school, put me in your desk, and the answers will be yours," the monster said.

Cooper picked up the card with two pencils. He didn't want to touch it. "What do I have to do in return?" he asked.

The slimy, wart-covered monster smiled. Its teeth looked like daggers.

"I just want to eat your classmates," said the monster. "I won't eat you. I promise."

On the day of the test,

_____

_____

_____

_____

_____

_____

_____

_____

_____

_____

_____

The End

The Second-Grade Vampire

By _____

Francis was trying to wake up. She shook the dream from her head, but it wouldn't go away. She was dreaming about school. "How boring!" she said, yawning. The morning light seemed to cut through her eyelids like lasers. While holding her hands up for protection, she slowly opened her eyes. Then she gasped. Who was that strange man standing over her? And why was he holding a stake and a hammer?

"The monster is waking!" the man screamed. Francis sat up. Behind the man were dozens more people, all holding stakes and hammers.

"Get her! Get her!" they all cried at once.

Francis leaped out of the long wooden box and began to run. She _____

_____

_____

_____

_____

_____

_____

_____

_____

_____

_____

_____

_____

_____

_____

_____

_____

_____

_____

_____

_____

The End

The Museum of Blood

By _____

One cold, rainy day Miss O'Shady's second-grade class went on a field trip to the Museum of Natural History.

It was dark and damp inside the museum, and it was almost empty. Miss O'Shady told the class to wait in the Bat Room. She walked around the corner to buy tickets for a special show. The children looked around the room. Creepy-looking stuffed bats hung by fishing line from the ceiling.

"Nothing but dead animals in here," said a boy named Jose. "I think I'm going to die of boredom."

Just then, the lights began to flicker on and off. From the other room, the class heard Miss O'Shady's shrill, terror-filled scream.

"Oh, you won't die of BOREDOM," the kids heard a deep voice say overhead. Suddenly, some of the stuffed bats came to life and swooped down toward the children.

Most of the kids ran, but Jose stood still long enough to watch a bat turn into a vampire! Blood dripped from his

fangs. "And you, sweet child, will be dessert!" the vampire said.

Jose _____

_____

_____

_____

_____

_____

_____

_____

_____

_____

_____

_____

_____

_____

_____

The End

On the next few pages, you will find the beginnings and endings of stories. You have to write the middles. Remember to make them scary!

Little Bloody Riding Hood

By _____

Once there lived a little girl called Little White Riding Hood. She always wore a white cape and hood made for her by her grandmother. Even though life was hard and her family never had enough food, Little White Riding Hood was always strong and healthy, her cheeks rosy and chubby.

One evening, as she was skipping through the woods on her way to her grandmother's house, a vicious wolf jumped onto the path and showed his pointy teeth.

"A little snack before dinner," said the wolf, snarling.

"Just what I was thinking," said Little White Riding Hood, revealing HER razor-sharp fangs.

The wolf _____

_____

_____

_____

_____

_____

_____

_____

_____

_____

_____

_____

_____

_____

And from that day on, people called her Little Red Riding Hood, and they never knew that it was blood, not berries, that had stained her white cape and hood.

The End

Slimy Locks and the Three Bears

By _____

Once upon a time there were three bears: Mama Bear, Papa Bear, and Baby Bear. Papa had whipped up some nice porridge for breakfast, but it was too hot. So Mama Bear suggested they take their bowls and go sit by the lake, where the breeze would cool the porridge faster.

"Baby Bear, you pick out a spot for us to sit," said Mama Bear. And Baby Bear did.

But Papa Bear said, "My spot is too far from the lake."

And Mama Bear said, "My spot is too far from the lake, too."

And Baby Bear said, "I hear there is a sea monster that lives in the lake. Its head is covered with slime, and it likes to snack on picnickers who sit too close to the edge, so my spot is JUST RIGHT!"

Mama and Papa Bear laughed at Baby Bear. "Only a child would believe such stories," said Mama Bear. And they both moved to the edge of the lake and left Baby Bear behind.

Soon _____

_____

_____

_____

_____

_____

_____

_____

_____

_____

_____

_____

_____

_____

_____

_____

_____

Thanks to Baby Bear, Mama Bear only had a few
scratches, but Papa Bear was eaten alive. After that horrible
morning, the lake was drained, but the monster they called
Slimy Locks was not there. It was never seen again.

The End

The Hands and Gretel

By _____

In a little town at the edge of a forest lived a poor little girl named Gretel. She was all alone in the world because her twin brother, Hansel, had been lost in the forest and was never heard from again. Afterward, Gretel's parents were so sad, they were unable to take care of her.

One day the little girl was working in her tiny garden when she heard something moving at the edge of the tall grass. What looked like two little brown bunnies made their way toward her. She smiled until she saw it was not a pair of bunnies but a pair of hands! She screamed. The hands wanted her to follow them. Just then, Gretel noticed a little ring made of twigs on one of the fingers. It was the same ring she had made for her brother, Hansel!

"Hansel?" she asked.

The fingers waggled at her.

"Where is the rest of you?" she cried.

The hands turned around and scampered into the forest. Gretel followed and _____

_____

_____

_____

_____

_____

_____

_____

_____

_____

_____

_____

Gretel was able to reverse the witch's curse for Hansel and all the other children who were thought to be dead. When Gretel told the townspeople how she got rid of the wicked witch, they thanked her and gave her a big party. There, Hansel and Gretel danced hand in hand, and they lived happily ever after.

The End

Down the Drain

By _____

The plumber sat at the Flemings' kitchen table and shook his head. "According to my records, Mr. Fleming," he said, "plumbing repairs have been started many times on this house but never completed. Do you know why?"

Mr. Fleming just wanted the terrible plumbing problems to end. Faucets had exploded, and ice cubes often came out of them instead of hot water. And yesterday, Mrs. Fleming had taken a shower in what looked like blood!

"Please just fix everything," Mr. Fleming said, and he left the room.

The plumber took out a long, narrow metal tube and began fishing around in the sink drain. There was something in there, all right, but what? Suddenly, the tube was yanked from below so hard, the plumber's hand went down the drain and became stuck.

"Help me!" cried the plumber. "Something is eating my hand!"

_____

_____

_____

_____

_____

_____

_____

_____

_____

_____

_____

_____

_____

_____

The Flemings moved out of the house the next day. No one ever found out what had really happened to the plumber, or what it was he had found.

The End

The Liar's Tongue

By _____

Judy was a little girl who had a bad habit of telling lies. She didn't mean to lie. It just made it easier for her to get what she wanted, so the lies kept slipping out. One day Judy went to a carnival and saw a fortune-teller's tent. She wanted to have her fortune told, so she lied and said she had money to pay. The old woman told Judy her fortune. When it came time to pay, Judy confessed that she had no money. The old woman became very angry, but Judy had gotten what she wanted.

The next day at school, Judy was telling her teacher a lie about why she didn't have her homework. All of a sudden the inside of her mouth felt furry, and she started to slur her words. "What's happening to my tongue?" Judy wondered as her tongue started to grow. The teacher _____

_____

_____

_____

_____

_____

_____

_____

_____

_____

_____

_____

_____

_____

And that's how Judy was swallowed by her own tongue.

The End

Here, draw a picture to go with the middle of your story.

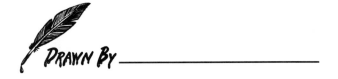 DRAWN BY _____

The Diet and Exercise Zombie

By _____

Lately, all Marco's mom wanted to do was diet and exercise. It seemed like a trance had come over her ever since she had hired a strange, smelly nanny to help around the house. Whenever Marco's mom wasn't looking, the nanny would pull Marco's ears! And when she made soup, she put things like maggots and rat's hair in it. Marco never ate it, but his mom did, because the weird nanny told her it was diet soup. Marco's mom was becoming a diet and exercise zombie! He decided to

_____

_____

_____

_____

_____

_____

_____

_____

_____

_____

_____

_____

_____

_____

_____

_____

Marco watched his mom slurp down the soup he had made. She had no idea of the horrors that had gone on the night before.

"I'm starting to feel better already," said his mom. "Thanks for making this tasty soup. By the way, where is Nanny?"

Marco didn't answer. He just stared at the soup.

The End

The Night Visitors

By _____

Stephanie woke up to a terrible silence. There were no noises in the house: no ticking clocks, no air blowing from the vents, no drips, no creaks, no coughs or squeaks. There was only a light so bright, she could not see what lifted her from her bed and carried her toward her second-floor window.

"Mom!" she cried, but no sound came out. Whatever was moving her had several hands! Stephanie _____

_____

_____

_____

_____

_____

A hundred years later, the letter
Stephanie had written to her parents
reached Stephanie's own great-great-
grandchildren. It said, "Having
fun. Wish you were here."

Having fun.
Wish you were
here.
Stephanie

The End

write the beginning

On the next few pages, you will find the middles and endings of stories. You have to write the beginnings! Remember to make them scary!

A Table for Terror

By _____

_____
_____
_____
_____
_____
_____
_____
_____
_____
_____
_____
_____
_____
_____

    Kim was beginning to regret that she had made such a fuss about being hungry. Once her eyes adjusted to the darkness, she could see that the place was empty, except for the Lee family.

    "The sign said 'OPEN,'" grumbled Mr. Lee.

"Let's leave," said Kim.

"No, wait," Mr. Lee said, waving his hand at his daughter. "We are customers, and we deserve to be treated with respect." He stood up and tugged firmly at his shirt. "I will be back with a waiter to take our order."

Mr. Lee disappeared around the corner, where a red light lit up the old, dirty brown floor. Kim and her sister, Lily, fidgeted. Mrs. Lee looked worried. After several minutes, she stood up.

"Don't leave us here alone!" wailed Lily.

"Don't be silly," said Mrs. Lee. "I'll just find your father and tell him we want to go. We are wasting good sight-seeing time."

Mrs. Lee turned the corner and disappeared.

Lily and Kim waited and waited and waited.

"Where are mother and father?" said Kim to Lily. "They went back into the restaurant's kitchen a long time ago."

"And what were those noises?" said Lily. "Is the cook strangling cats for our dinner?"

"We better go check," they both said at once. And, unfortunately, they did.

The End

The Mischievous Markers

By _____

_____

_____

_____

_____

_____

_____

_____

_____

_____

_____

_____

_____

_____

_____

_____

_____

Vanya and Maria watched Daisy's parents cry. The children felt terrible when they realized what they had done. Sure, Daisy had been mean and sometimes cruel, but did she deserve to disappear so suddenly?

Vanya and his sister wished they had never found the pack of markers. The pens had seemed a perfect way to get even with the mean kids who had teased Vanya and Maria about their parents. But now the children wished they could get rid of the markers forever.

"I have an idea!" said Vanya, and he grabbed the evil markers from Maria, who was crying. First he drew a picture of Daisy. Then he drew a picture of the whole pack of markers, and he threw the picture into the fireplace. As the picture burned, the evil markers on the table turned to ashes, and Daisy appeared again.

The End

The Really Bad Hair Day

By _____

_____

_____

_____

_____

_____

_____

_____

_____

_____

_____

_____

_____

_____

_____

_____

_____

"How could this have happened?" Gabby asked herself as her classmates ran, yelling, from the room. A moment ago, the boy behind her had suddenly turned blue and started choking. Fearfully, Gabby knelt next to the pale, barely breathing student. Wrapped around his neck were long golden strands of strong, ropelike hair—HER hair! Gabby's new hair!

Gabby used to have nice blond hair. When she wished for really long, beautiful hair, she was thrilled that her dream came true. But now her dream had turned into a nightmare! Gabby had to do something, or her hair might try to strangle everyone in Middletown Elementary School!

Screaming like a warrior, Gabby wrestled her hair to the ground. After grabbing scissors off her teacher's desk, she chopped and chopped at her hair until it lay on the floor in heaps. Then she threw it into her book bag and rushed home to burn the hair in the fireplace. Then, to be safe, her father helped her to shave the rest of the evil hair off her head, until she was bald.

"I'll never wish to be different again!" Gabby promised. And she never did.

The End

Gargoyles Just Want to Have Fun

By _____

_____

_____

_____

_____

_____

_____

_____

_____

Brad picked up a rock. He looked around. The teacher was busy talking to King George in front of the castle.

"I bet I can hit that ugly gargoyle right in its crooked old eye," said Brad, squinting one eye to aim.

"Better not," said Brenda. "This castle is supposed to be haunted!"

Brad laughed. "Whoa, I'm shaking. Someone get my mommy!"

"Let's catch up," Brenda pleaded. "Why do you want to throw rocks, anyway?"

"I just want to have a little fun!" said Brad.

Brad had a good arm. The rock hit the stone gargoyle right in the eye.

And just as the rock hit, there was a terrifying screech that echoed through the castle grounds. Even the kids ahead with the teacher stopped and looked around.

Brenda ran away.

"It's just a crow!" Brad yelled after her. But then he heard a crumbling sound, and soon bits of stone began to fall on him. He looked up just in time to see the stone gargoyle stretch its massive legs and shake rock dust off its large black wings.

"Help! Help!" cried Brad, but his classmates had already turned the corner and were out of sight.

CRASH! CRASH! CRASH! One after the other, the stone gargoyles lining the castle wall stood and raised their wings, until Brad was faced with an army of grinning monsters.

The gargoyle holding its eye said in a squeaky voice, "Gargoyles just want to have fun, too!"

And they all swept down on poor Brad, who was too scared to run. No one missed him until the class got back to the bus. They searched and searched, but Brad was never found.

The End

The Troll Bridge

By _____

_____

_____

_____

_____

_____

_____

_____

_____

_____

_____

_____

Danny shook his head as if shaking a dust ball from his brain. He had been right! It was the pine-needle stew that had made him and the other children so weak. Without the stew, the Trolls wouldn't be able to wrestle a baby!

For the next few days Danny pretended to eat the stew. Then he began to get each of the other children to stop eating it. Day by day the children began to free themselves from the evil Trolls' spell.

One day Danny gave the signal. He tripped the Troll guard, stole his keys, and escaped from his cage. Then he pushed the guard into the huge boiling pot of pine-needle stew. Danny quickly freed the other children from their tiny prisons.

"We're free! We're free!" they all squealed.

Danny looked at the crowd of children around him. He had grown almost five inches since the day long ago when the evil Trolls had snatched him from his dad's car under the Troll bridge. He was stronger, too, from carrying the Trolls' packs and water like a slave. The Trolls had made slaves of all the stolen children.

"There are enough of us now," Danny whispered. "We can stick together to fight off the rest of the Trolls, then find our way home. There, we can get help to destroy the evil Trolls and their bridge forever."

Later, the children walked away from the Trolls' camp, leaving the rest of the Trolls behind in the cages the children had called home for the past five years.

The End

Spaghetti and Murder

By _____

_____

_____

_____

_____

_____

_____

_____

_____

_____

_____

_____

_____

_____

_____

_____

Then I realized she wasn't serving spaghetti—she was serving snakes! And those weren't meatballs—they were eyeballs! I closed the huge refrigerator door in horror. When I turned to run, there stood the cafeteria cook, a knife as long as a baseball bat in her hand.

"Tomorrow for lunch—Hamburger Patty!" she said with a cackle, lunging at me. I dodged her, and she fell into a huge tub of Jell-O that was about to thicken. She screamed and wiggled in the thickening goo.

"Quick!" I cried to the other kids. "Help me put this tub in the refrigerator!"

Eight hours later, the crazy cafeteria cook had become a gelatin mold. She finally got her "just desserts."

The End

are you scary or not?

You've come a long way from when you took the **How Scary Are You?** quiz. You've probably learned a lot about what's scary and what's not. Or have you? Before you move on to the **Advanced Exercises,** you'd better take one more test!

Example:
You hear a noise in the bathroom. You pull back the shower curtain and see a bug. If it is <u>ten feet tall</u>, it IS scary. If it is <u>a dead ant</u>, it is NOT scary!

SCARY!   **YAWN . . .**

Now you try it!

You are walking alone through the woods late at night when you hear someone calling your name. If it is a _____, it IS scary. If it is a _____, it is NOT scary!

You are going through your grandpa's drawer when you find a lucky rabbit's foot on a key chain. If it _____, it IS scary. If it _____, it is NOT scary!

A man walks past a store window on a stormy night. He is stopped by something he sees in the window. He stares at it, although it is raining hard. If he suddenly _____, it IS scary. If he suddenly _____, it is NOT scary!

A baby closes its eyes and concentrates. If it _____, it IS scary. If it _____, it is NOT scary!

advanced exercise

Anything can be spooky if you want it to be! Advanced scary story writers should study the facts listed below. Your job: Use the facts to make your story scary! Do the same on the pages that follow. Use more paper if you need to.

Who: three friends

What: sneak out the window at a slumber party

When: at midnight

Where: in Transylvania

Why: they dared each other

Title: _____

By _____

_____

_____

_____

_____

_____

_____

_____

_____

_____

_____

_____

Who: an astronaut

What: sneaks into a spaceship

When: in the future

Where: in the Milky Way Galaxy

Why: he wants revenge

Title: _____

By _____

_____

_____

_____

_____

_____

_____

_____

_____

_____

_____

_____

_____

_____

advanced exercise

Who: an old lady

What: stands by the road and cries

When: whenever it rains

Where: in a big city

Why: she lost something

Title: _____

By _____

_____

_____

_____

_____

_____

_____

_____

_____

_____

_____

_____

_____

_____

advanced exercise

On the next two pages, make up your own story or stories, or use the extra space to continue a favorite story in this book. Draw a picture on the last page to go with what you write. Happy haunting!

_____

_____

_____

_____

_____

_____

_____

_____

_____

_____

_____

_____

_____

_____

_____

_____

_____

_____

_____

DRAWN BY _____